# Bastiens' Invitation to Music

**For:**
Age 4 and up

**Time:**
A Lifetime of Enjoyment

**Hosts:**
Jane Smisor Bastien
Lisa Bastien
Lori Bastien

**KJOS**

Neil A. Kjos
Music Company,
Publisher

## BOOK D
# THEORY & EAR TRAINING PART

## CONTENTS

Pianos, Sheet Music, Musical Instruments

**Stanger's**
THE MUSIC PEOPLE
5, CATHERINE STREET, SALISBURY
Telephone Salisbury 322278

ISBN 0-8497-9560-5

MUSIC·LINK
£4.95

# UNIT 1

# MUSICAL MERMAID

Color:
- B's red
- C's yellow
- E's green
- D's orange
- F's blue
- A's pink
- G's purple

# SHARPS AND FLATS

Write both letter names of each shaded key.

**1.**
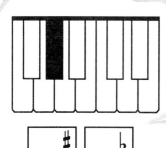

**2.**
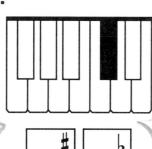

**3.**
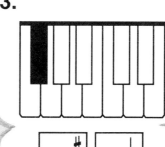

**4.**
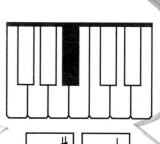

Color the keys indicated below. Play them on the keyboard.

**1.**
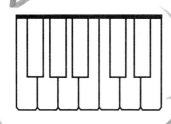

E♭

**2.**
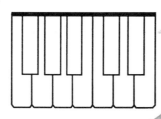

C♯

**3.**
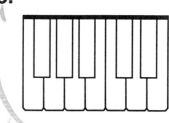

C♭

**4.**
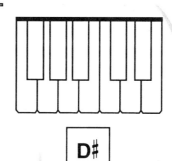

D♯

**5.**
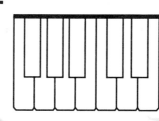

G♭

# LADYBUG INTERVALS

Connect each interval to its correct ladybug.

# MINOR POSITIONS

1. Unscramble the letters to form the following minor 5-finger positions.
2. Write the letters in the triangles.

c minor: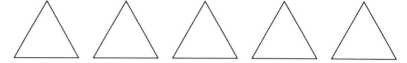

g minor: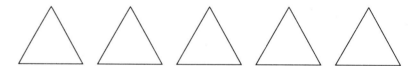

f minor: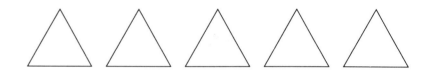

3. Write letters on the keyboards to form the minor 5-finger positions.
4. Color the keys ■ red to form minor one chords.

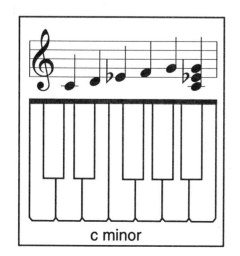

c minor

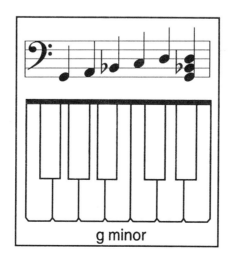

g minor

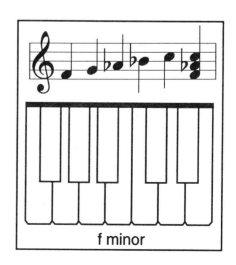

f minor

# BIRTHDAYS, SAINTS, BRIDES, OR STARS?

# TAP AND CLAP FILL-INS

1.
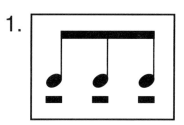 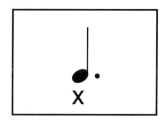 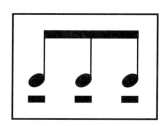 

2.
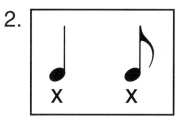 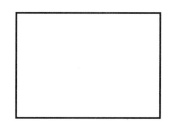 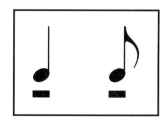 

3.
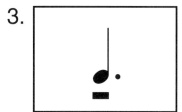 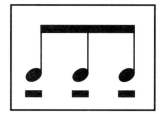  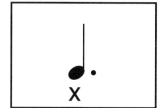

4.
 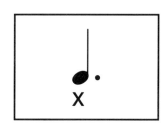 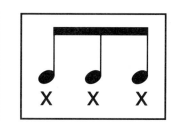 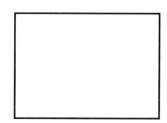

**WP277**

**UNIT 2**

# DREAMING MICE

1. In $\frac{4}{4}$, color the **mice** with notes and rests that receive:
   - ■ one count brown
   - ■ two counts black
   - ■ three counts pink
   - ■ four counts gray
2. In $\frac{6}{8}$, color the **cheese** with notes and rests that receive:
   - ■ one count yellow
   - ■ two counts orange
   - ■ three counts green
   - ■ six counts blue

# WRITING THE SHARPS

1. The sharps are always written in the same order on the staff.

F  C  G  D  A  E  B

2. Do you see the box in the middle of the sharp?

**The box has either a line going through it**    OR    **the box is in a space between two lines.**

3. Write the order of sharps two times below. Say the letters aloud as you write.

1.                2.

# NOTE PARTY

1. Write the letter names of the notes in the triangles.
2. Play the notes in the correct place on the keyboard.

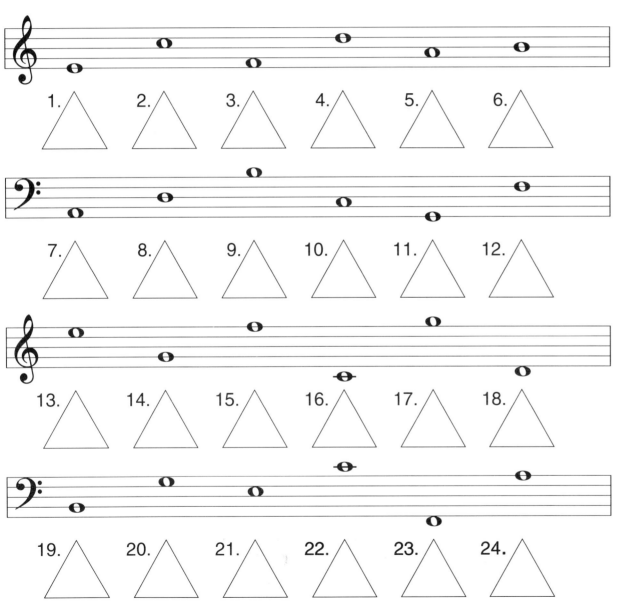

# D POSITIONS AND CHORDS

1. Unscramble the letters to form the **D Major** and **d minor** 5-finger positions.
2. Write the letters in the triangles.

D Major: △ △ △ △ △

d minor: △ △ △ △ △

3. Write letters on the keyboards to form the D positions.
4. Color the keys ■ blue to form Major and minor one chords.

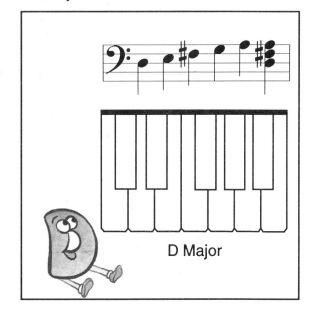

D Major

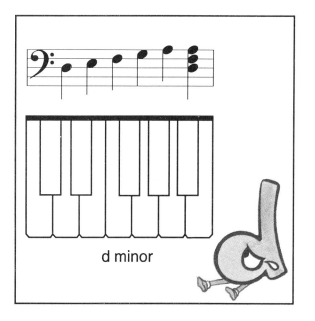

d minor

**WP277**

# BIRTHDAYS, SAINTS, BRIDES, OR STARS?

# HAPPY OR SAD?

**1.**

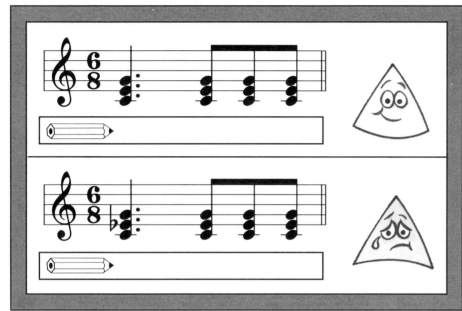

**2.**

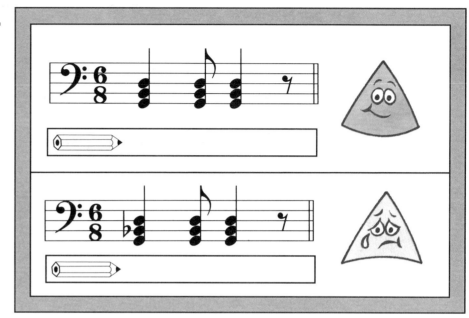

**3.**

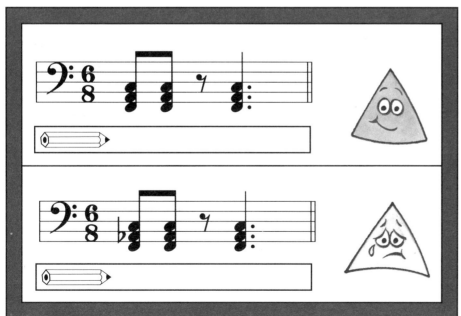

Write the number of counts each of the following notes and rests receive in $\frac{6}{8}$.

♩ = ☐          ♪ = ☐

♩. = ☐          𝄾. = ☐

𝄾 = ☐          ♩. = ☐

# UNIT 3   NAMING SHARP KEY SIGNATURES

Write the order of sharps three times below.
Say the letters aloud as you write.

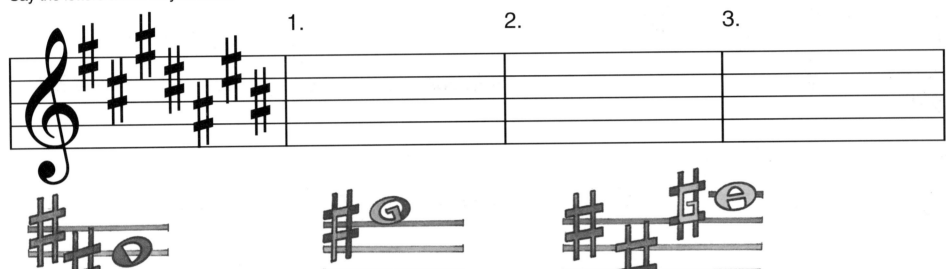

1.   2.   3.

**FINDING THE KEY**✱

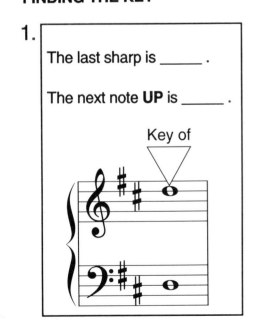

1.

The last sharp is _____ .

The next note **UP** is _____ .

Key of

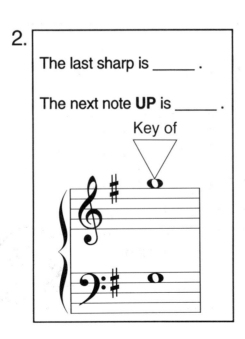

2.

The last sharp is _____ .

The next note **UP** is _____ .

Key of

3.

The last sharp is _____ .

The next note **UP** is _____ .

Key of

4.

✱**EXCEPTION:** The key of C has **no** sharps.

# A POSITIONS AND CHORDS

1. Unscramble the letters to form the **A Major** and **a mino**r 5-finger positions.
2. Write the letters in the triangles.

A Major: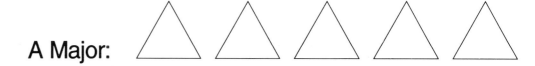

a minor:

3. Write letters on the keyboards to form the A 5-finger positions.
4. Color the keys ▮ red to form Major and minor one chords.

A Major

a minor

# RECOGNIZING INTERVALS

# RHYTHM AND CHORDS

**1.**

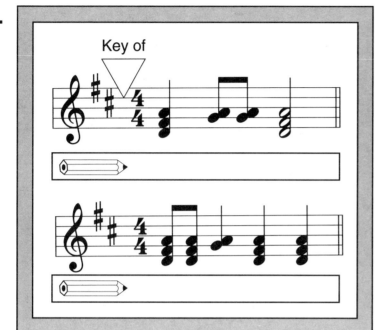

**2.**

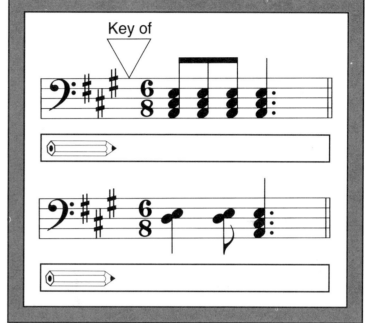

**3.**

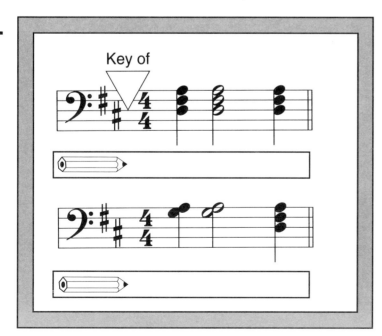

Write the number of counts each of the following notes and rests receive in $\frac{4}{4}$.

♩ =  ☐          ♩ =  ☐

𝄽 =  ☐          ▬ =  ☐

♫ =  ☐          o =  ☐

# SHARP KEY SIGNATURES

Write the order of sharps on the staff.

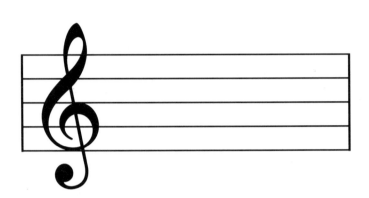

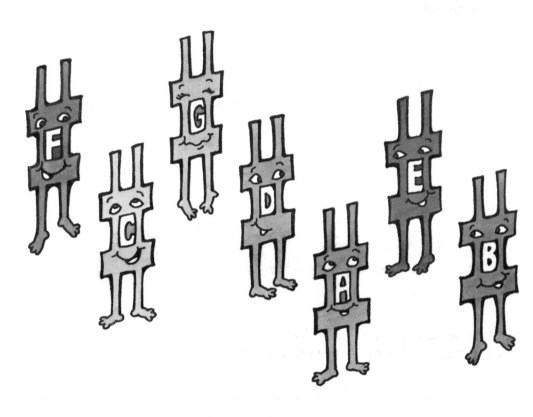

## FINDING THE KEY

**1.**
The last sharp is _____ .

The next note **UP** is _____ .

Key of

**2.**
The last sharp is _____ .

The next note **UP** is _____ .

Key of

**3.**
There are no sharps in this key signature!

Key of

**4.**
The last sharp is _____ .

The next note **UP** is _____ .

Key of

# E POSITIONS AND CHORDS

1. Unscramble the letters to form the **E Major** and **e minor** 5-finger positions.
2. Write the letters in the triangles.

E Major: △ △ △ △ △

e minor: △ △ △ △ △

3. Write letters on the keyboards to form the E positions.
4. Color the keys ▦ blue to form major and minor one chords.

E Major

e minor

WP277

# RECOGNIZING INTERVALS

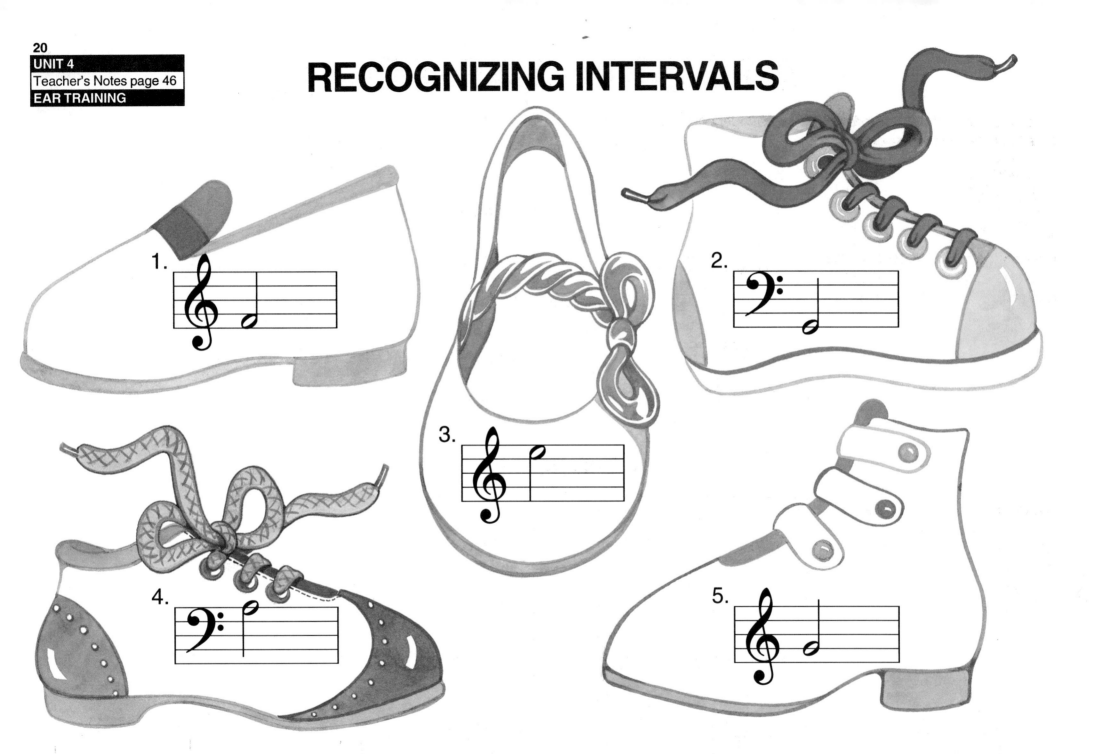

# RHYTHM AND CHORDS

**1.**

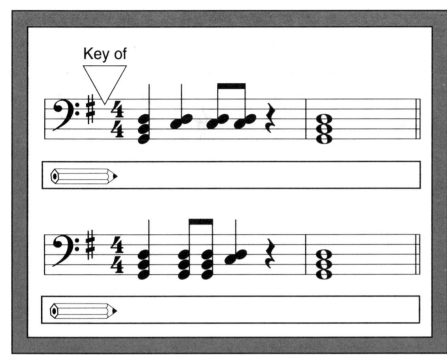

**2.**

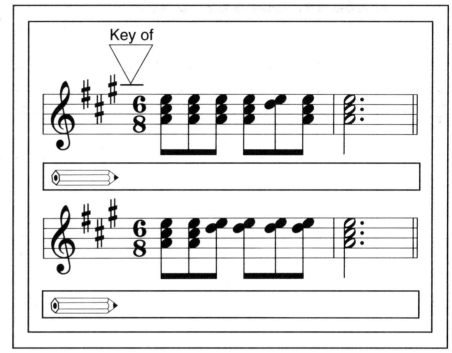

**3.**

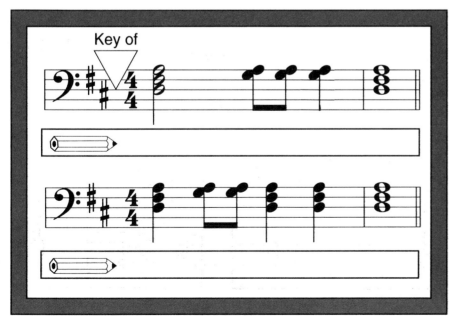

Write the number of counts each of the following notes and rests receive in $\frac{6}{8}$.

𝄽. = [ ]     𝄾 = [ ]

𝅗𝅥. = [ ]     ♩ = [ ]

♪ = [ ]     𝄾 = [ ]

# UNIT 5 — CHORDS AND KEYBOARDS

1. Write the letter names of the chords in the triangles.   2. On the keyboards, write letters to form each chord.

**1.**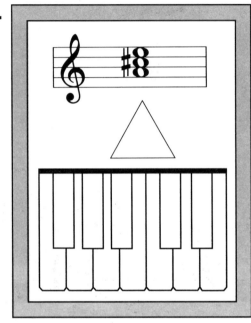

**2.**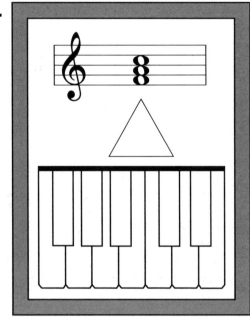

**3.**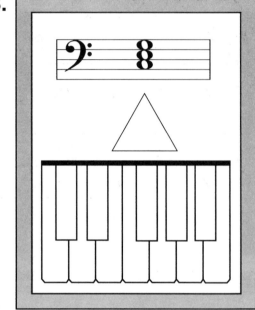

**4.**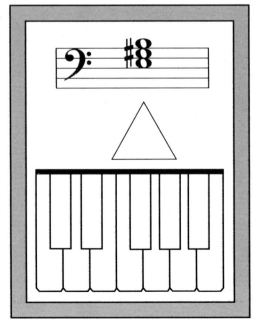

**5.**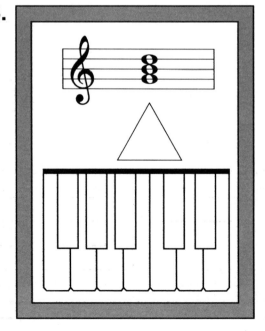

**6.**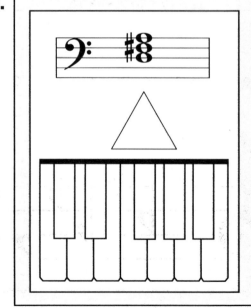

# WRITING THE FLATS

1. The flats are always written in the same order on the staff.

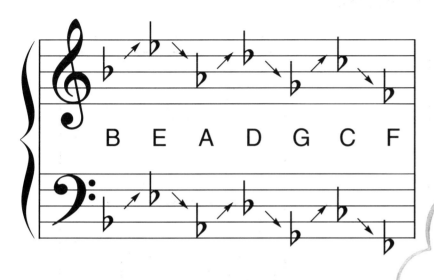

B  E  A  D  G  C  F

2. Do you see the rounded part of the flat?

**The rounded part has a line going through it** OR **the rounded part is in a space between two lines.**

3. Write the order of sharps two times below. Say the letters aloud as you write.

1.   2.

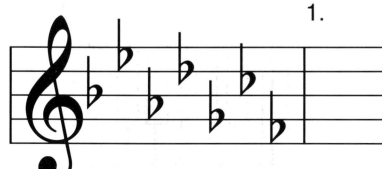

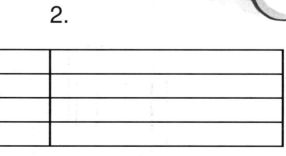

# INTERVAL PUZZLES

1. Write the letter name of each given note in the triangles.
2. Starting with the given note, complete each interval puzzle by writing the notes on the staff and the letters in the triangles as shown in the example.

Example:

1.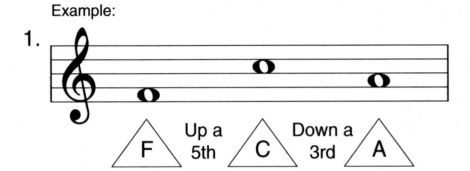

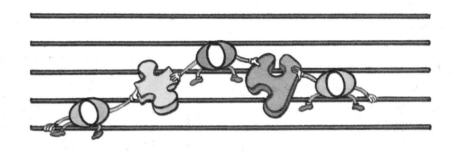

2.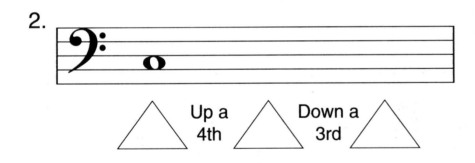

3.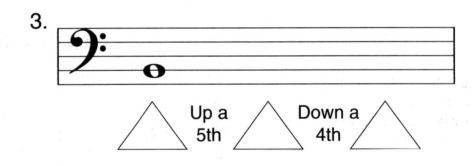

4.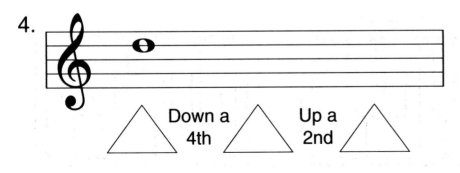

5.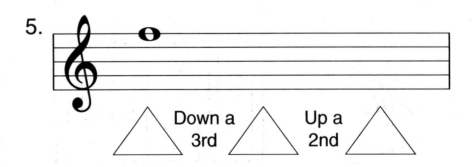

# D♭ POSITION AND CHORDS

1. Unscramble the letters below to form the **D♭ Major** 5-finger position.
2. Write the letters in the triangles.

D♭ Major: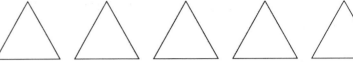

3. Write letters on the keyboard to form the D♭ Major 5-finger position.
4. Color the keys ■ red to form the D♭ Major I chord.

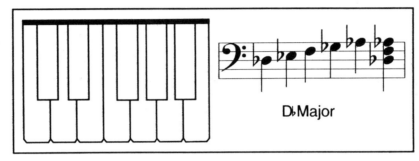

D♭ Major

## CHORD REVIEW

5. Write the letter names of the chords in the triangles.
6. On the keyboards, write letters to form each chord.

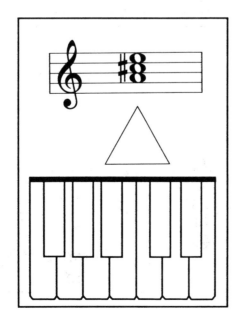

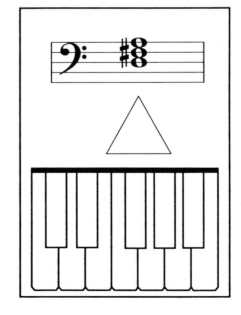

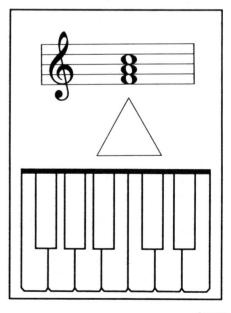

# RHYTHM AND CHORDS

**1.**

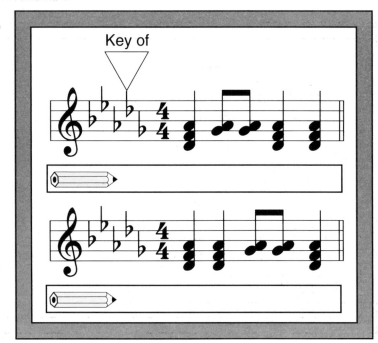

**2.**

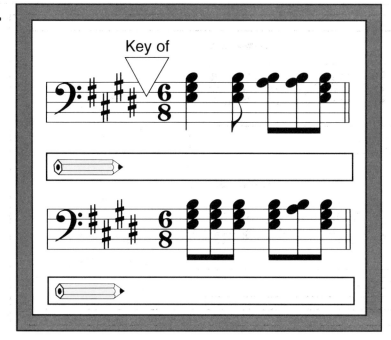

**3.**

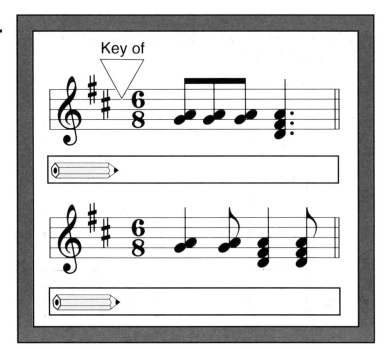

Write the number of counts each of the following notes and rests receive in $\frac{4}{4}$.

𝅝 = ☐          𝅗𝅥 = ☐

♫ = ☐          ♩ = ☐

𝄾 = ☐          ▬ = ☐

# HAPPY OR SAD?

**1.**

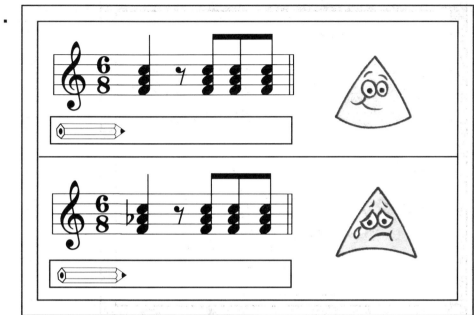

**2.**

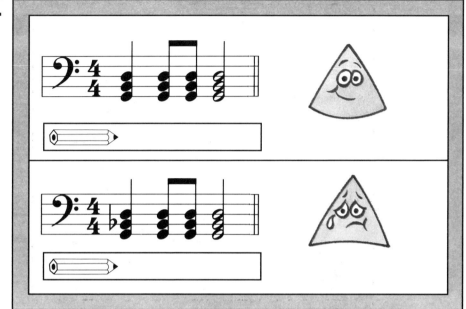

**3.**

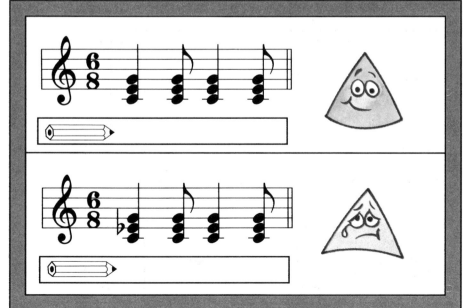

Write the number of counts each of the following notes and rests receive in $\frac{4}{4}$.

𝅝 =  ☐        𝅘𝅥𝅮𝅘𝅥𝅮 = ☐

𝅗𝅥 = ☐        𝄽 = ☐

𝄼 = ☐        𝅘𝅥 = ☐

# NAMING FLAT KEY SIGNATURES

Write the order of flats three times below.
Say the letters aloud as you write.

1.　　　　　2.　　　　　3.

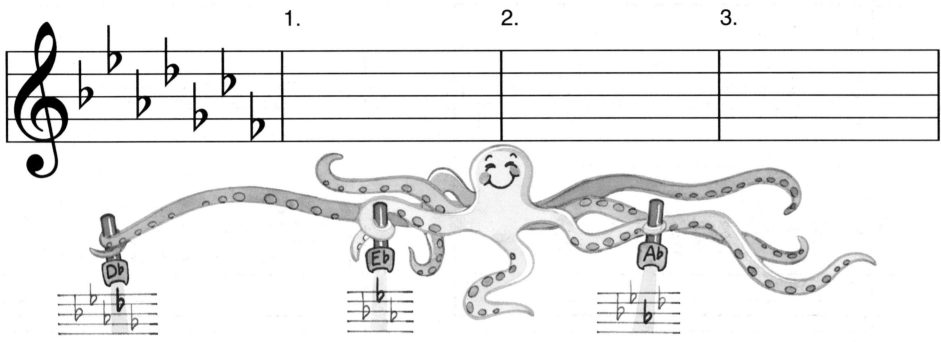

## FINDING THE KEY*

1. The next to last flat is_____.

Key of

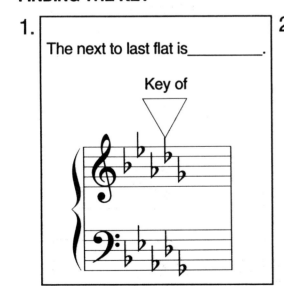

2. The next to last flat is_____.

Key of

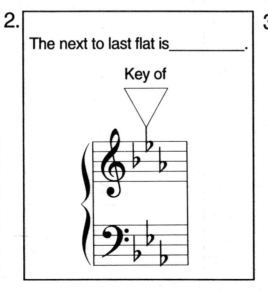

3. The next to last flat is_____.

Key of

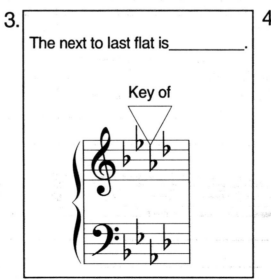

4. *EXCEPTION:

Key of

F (only one flat)

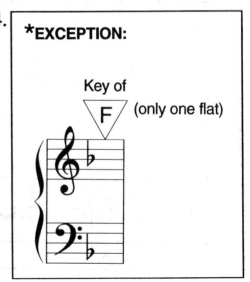

# A♭ POSITION AND CHORDS

1. Unscramble the letters to form the **A♭ Major** 5-finger position.
2. Write the letters in the triangles.

A♭ Major: △ △ △ △ △

3. Write the letters on the keyboard to form the A♭ Major 5-finger position.
4. Color the keys ■ red to form the A♭ Major I chord.

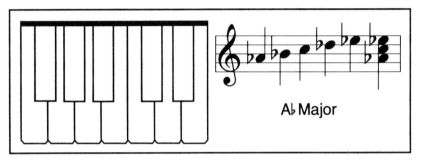

A♭ Major

## CHORD REVIEW

5. Write the letter names of the chords in the triangles.
6. On the keyboards, write letters to form each chord.

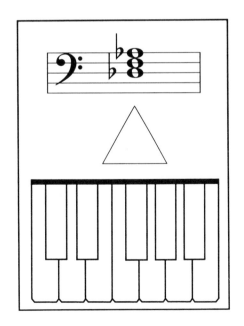

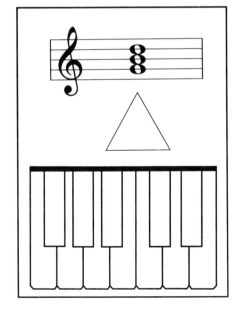

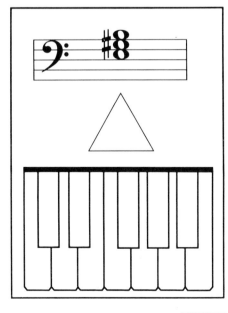

# BIRTHDAYS, SAINTS, BRIDES, OR STARS?

# RHYTHM AND CHORDS

**1.**

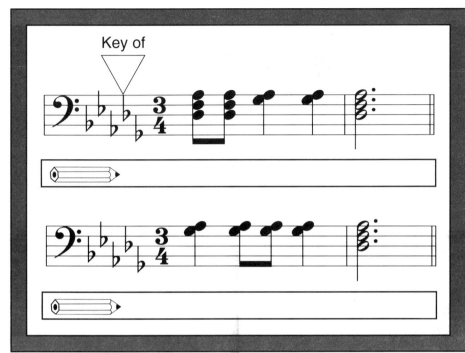

**2.**

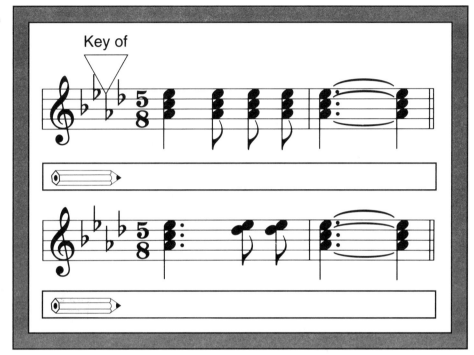

**3.**

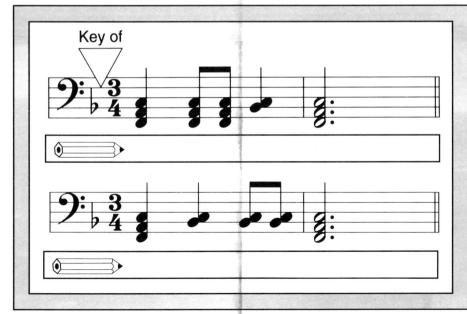

Write the number of counts each of the following notes and rests receive in $\frac{5}{8}$.

♪ = [ ]         𝄽 = [ ]

♩ = [ ]         ♩. ♩ = [ ]

♩. = [ ]

# HEARING MELODIES

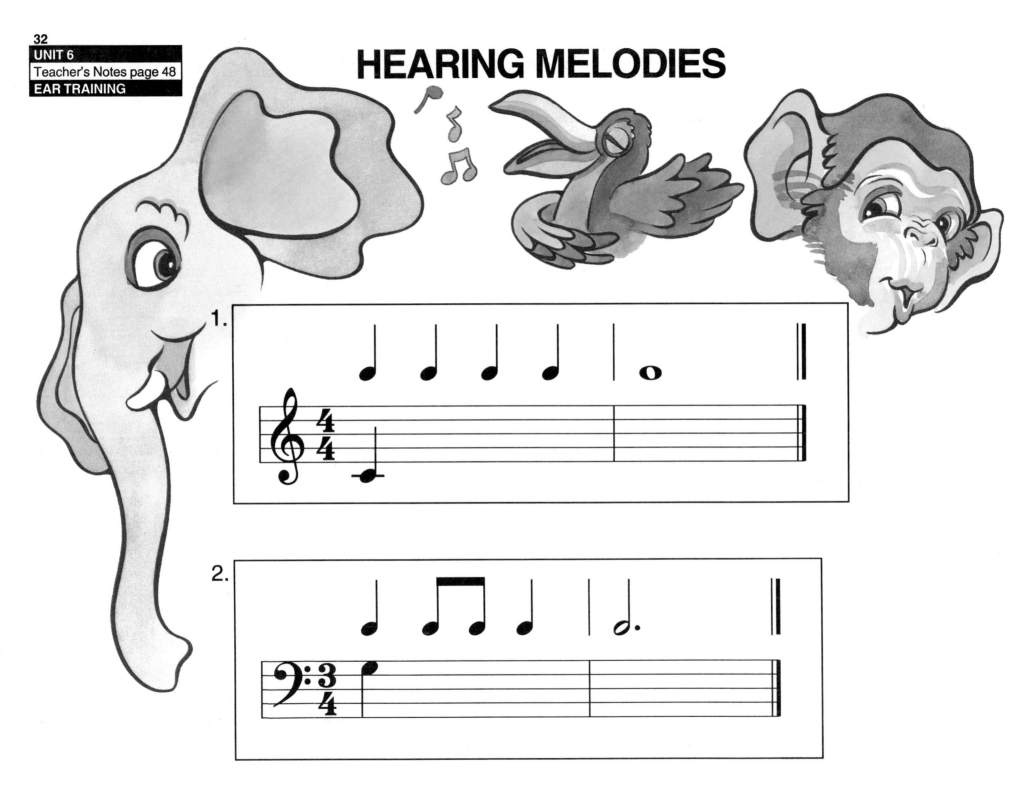

# FLAT KEY SIGNATURES

1. Write the order of flats on the staff.

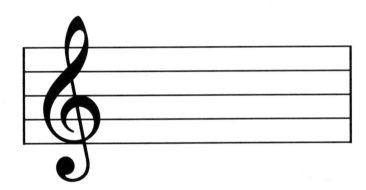

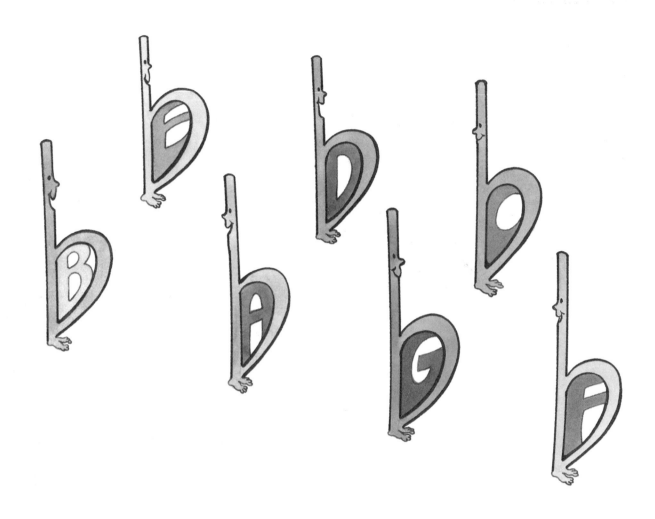

2. Write the letter names of the keys in the triangles.

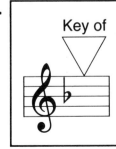
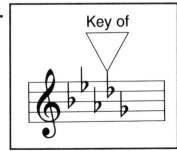
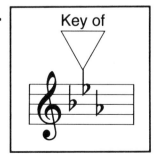
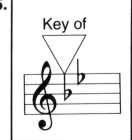

1. Key of

2. Key of

3. Key of

4. Key of

5. Key of

# SHARP KEY SIGNATURES

1. Write the order of sharps on the staff.

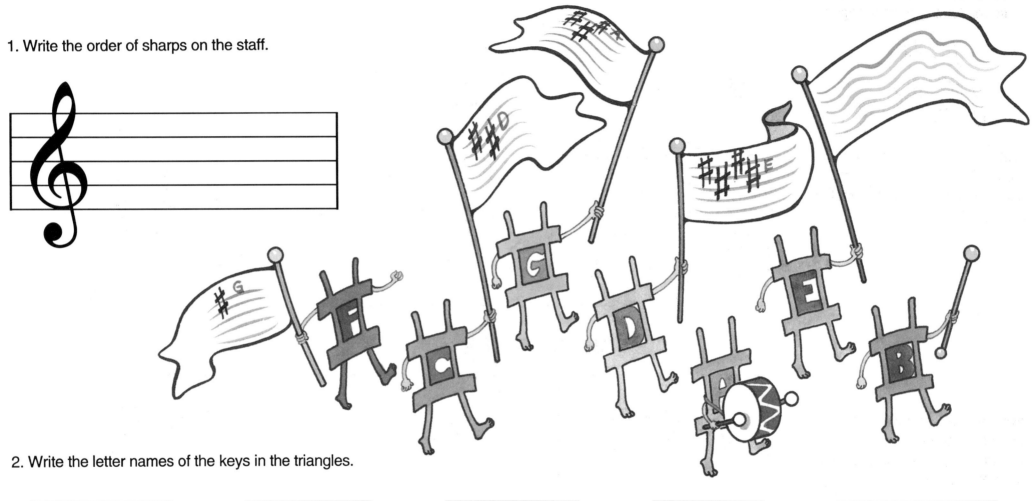

2. Write the letter names of the keys in the triangles.

1.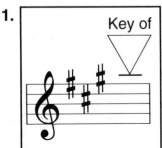
Key of

2.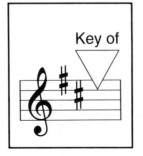
Key of

3.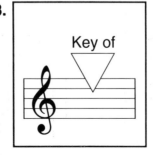
Key of

4.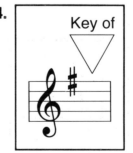
Key of

5.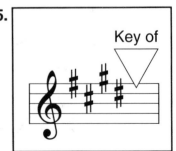
Key of

# E♭ POSITION AND CHORDS

1. Unscramble the letters to form the **E♭ Major** 5-finger position.
2. Write the letters in the triangles.

E♭ Major : △ △ △ △ △

3. Write letters on the keyboard to form the E♭ Major 5-finger position.
4. Color the keys ■ red to from the E♭ Major I chord.

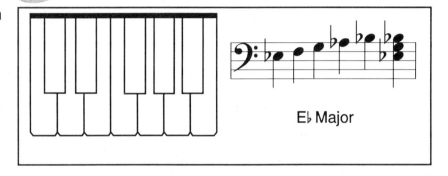

E♭ Major

## CHORD REVIEW

5. Write the letter names of the chords in the triangles.
6. On the keyboards, write letters to form each chord.

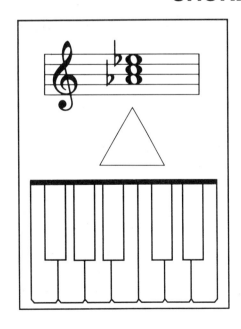

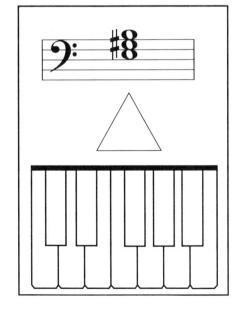

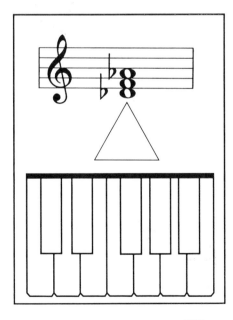

# HEARING MELODIES

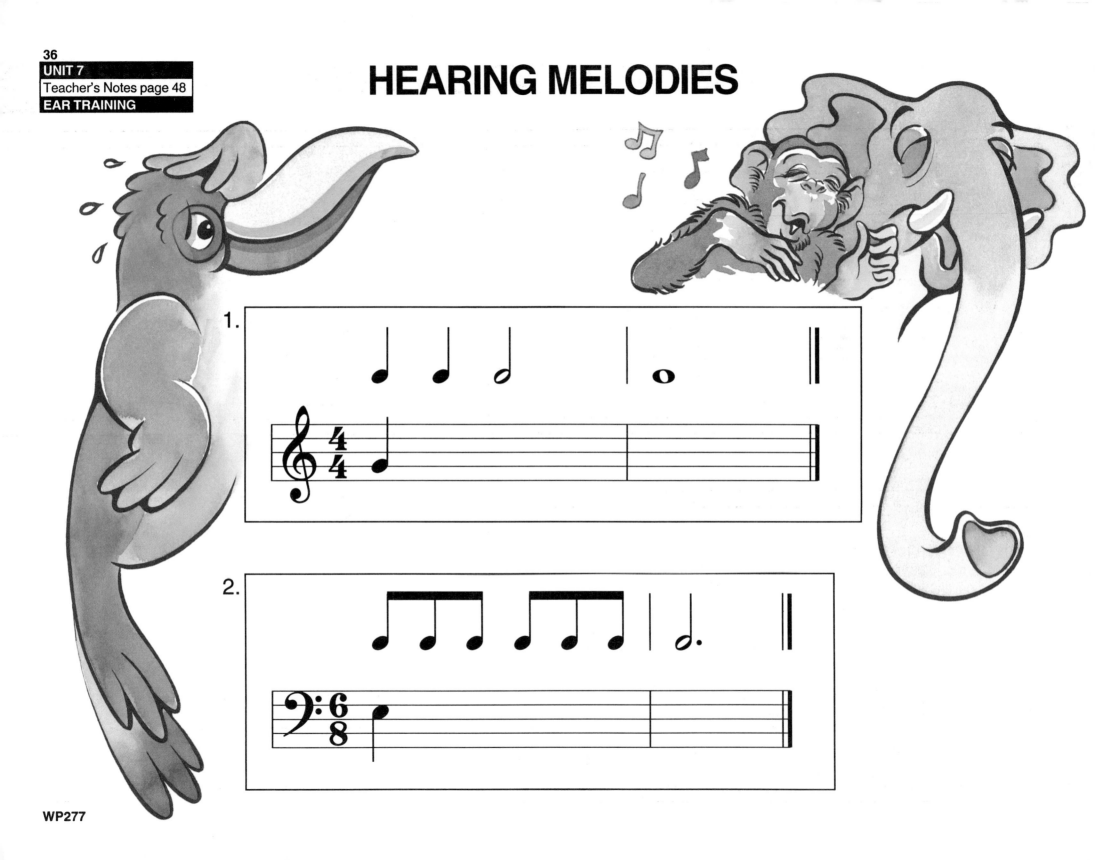

# RHYTHM AND CHORDS

**1.**

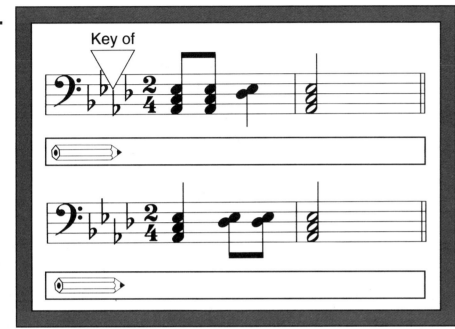

**2.**

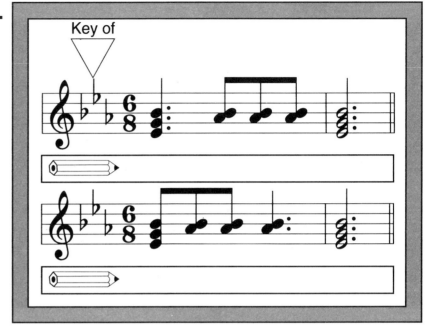

**3.**

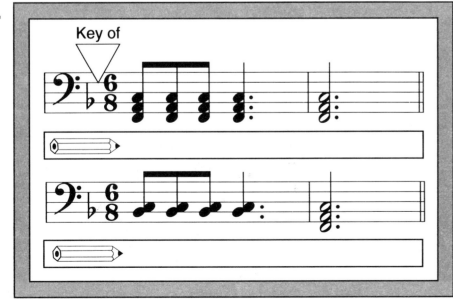

Write the number of counts each of the following notes and rests receive in $\frac{6}{8}$ .

♩ = ☐          𝄽 = ☐

♩. = ☐          𝅗𝅥. = ☐

𝄽 = ☐          ♪ = ☐

# HAPPY OR SAD?

**1.**

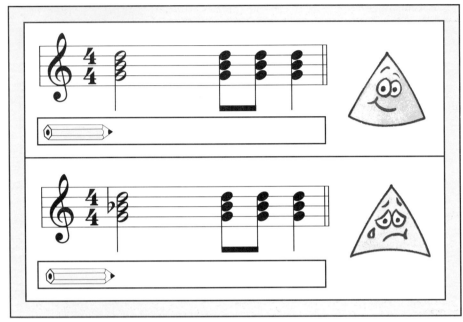

**2.**

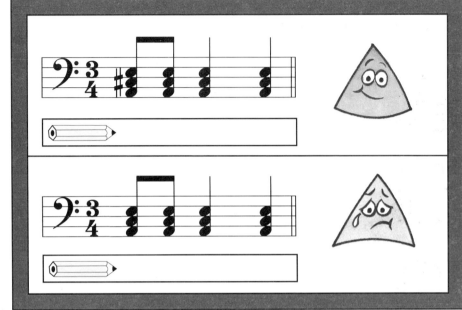

**3.**

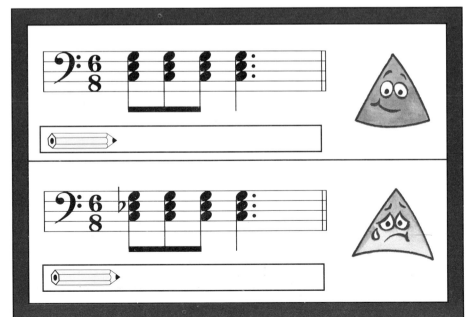

Write the number of counts each of the following notes and rests receive in $\frac{3}{4}$ .

# Gb, Bb, B POSITIONS AND CHORDS

1. Unscramble the letters to form the Major 5-finger positions.
2. Write the letters in the triangles.

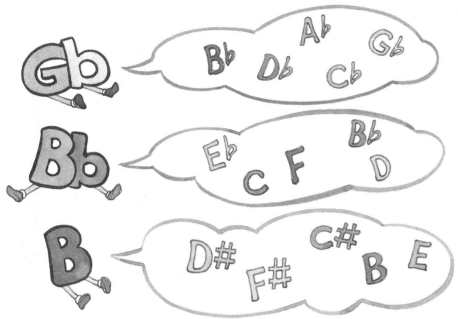

Gb Major:

Bb Major:

B Major:

3. Write letters on the keyboards to form the Major 5-finger positions.
4. Color the keys ■ red to form Major I chords for each position.

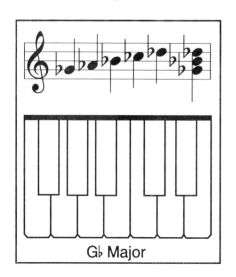

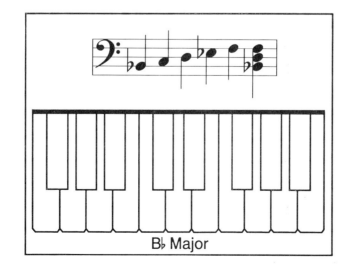

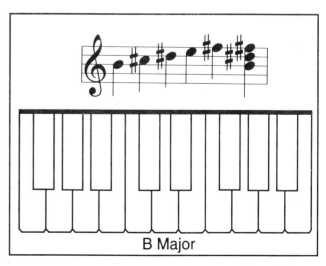

WP277

# NAME THE KEYS

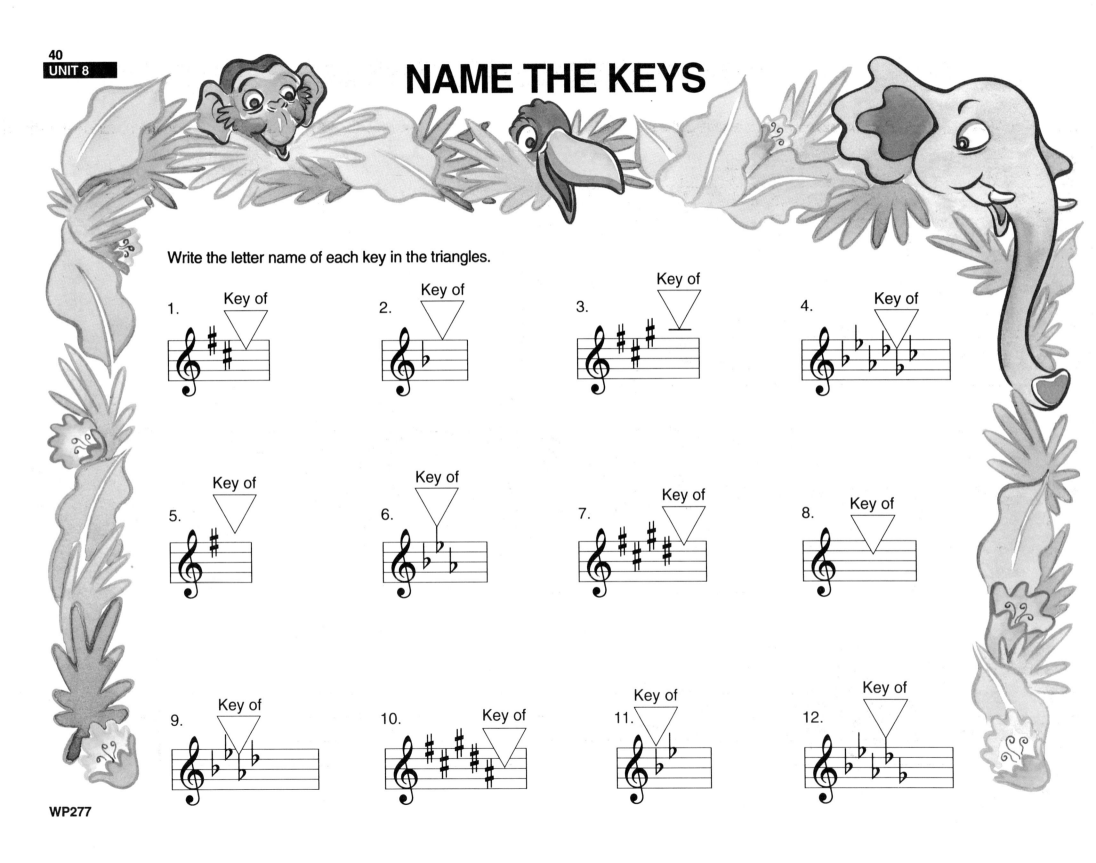

Write the letter name of each key in the triangles.

# MY SONG

_____     By _____
(Title)                                              (Draw your own picture below.)

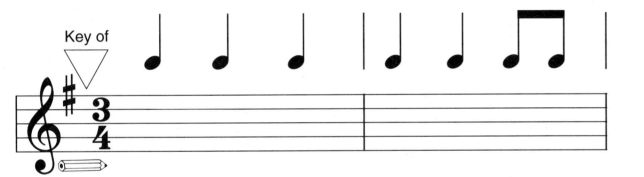

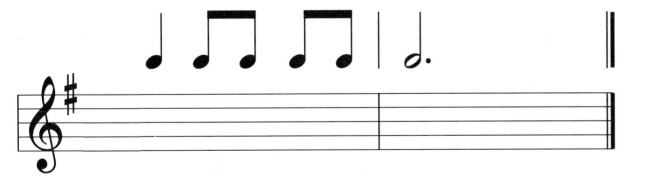

# GRAND FINALE!

1. Write the letter names of the chords in the triangles.
2. On the keyboards, write letters to form each chord.

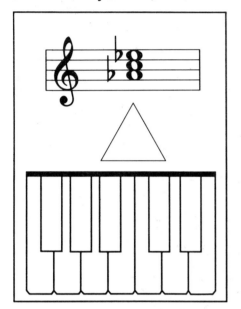 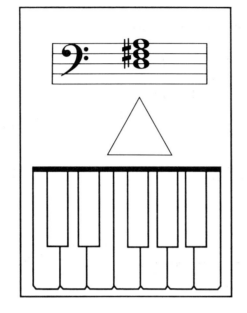 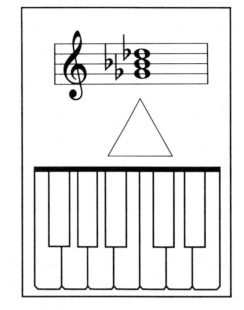 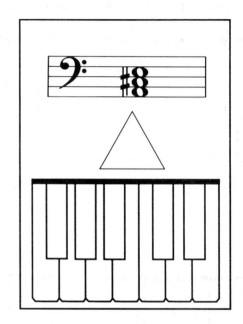

3. Write the counts for the following rhythms.
4. Clap and count the rhythms aloud.

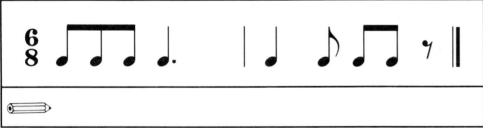 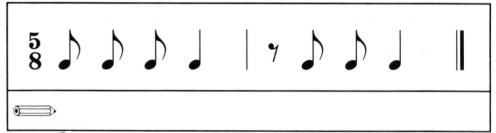

# GRAND FINALE!

5. Write the letters on the keyboards to form the Major 5-finger positions.
6. Color the keys ■ red to form Major I chords for each position.
7. Play Major and minor one chords for all keys below.

D Major

A Major

E Major

D♭ Major

A♭ Major

E♭ Major

G♭ Major

B♭ Major

B Major

WP277

# KEY SIGNATURE CARNIVAL

Write the letter name of each key in the triangles.

# TEACHER'S NOTES

*THEORY & EAR TRAINING PARTY* contains a variety of fun exercises to reinforce the concepts presented in *PIANO PARTY*. We suggest using these exercises with students after they have been introduced to the correlating weekly material in *PIANO PARTY*.

## UNIT 1 (pages 2-7)

### 5 MINOR POSITIONS

Minor is explained merely by position rather than by key signatures. To make a major key or chord minor, move the **middle finger DOWN** (left) to the nearest key.

### 6 BIRTHDAYS, SAINTS, BRIDES, OR STARS?

• Have the student write the names of the intervals in the triangles in all examples.

• To teach the sound of a specific interval, play and sing a familiar song that has that specific interval between the first two different pitches. Some suggestions:

  2nd: *Happy Birthday*
  3rd: *When the Saints Come Marching In*
  4th: *Here Comes the Bride*
  5th: *Twinkle, Twinkle, Little Star*

• Play each example three times:

  1. Have the student listen and determine what interval you played.
  2. Have the student listen again and circle the appropriate interval.
  3. Have the student check his or her answer after the third hearing.

### 7 TAP AND CLAP FILL-INS

• A fun way to portray or feel rhythm is to have students tap and clap:

  X = clap hands together

  ▬ = tap hands on the closed fallboard or in your lap

• Tap and clap each example three times:

  1. Have the student listen and repeat the taps and claps.
  2. Have the student listen again and fill in the missing notes.
  3. Have the student check his or her answer after the third hearing.

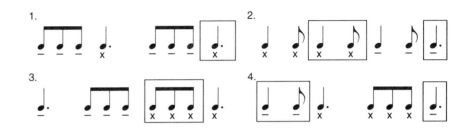

## UNIT 2 (pages 8-13)

### 12 BIRTHDAYS, SAINTS, BRIDES, OR STARS?

• Have the student write the names of the intervals in the triangles in all examples.

• To teach the sound of a specific interval, play and sing a familiar song that has that specific interval between the first two different pitches. Some suggestions:

  2nd: *Happy Birthday*
  3rd: *When the Saints Come Marching In*
  4th: *Here Comes the Bride*
  5th: *Twinkle, Twinkle, Little Star*

• Play each example three times:

  1. Have the student listen and determine what interval you played.
  2. Have the student listen again and circle the appropriate interval.
  3. Have the student check his or her answer after the third hearing.

### 13 HAPPY OR SAD?

• Have the student write the counts in all examples.

• As a warm-up exercise, play several Major and minor chords and have the student identify the qualities.

• Relate the happy face to the sound of Major chords and the sad face to the sound of minor chords.

*Continued on the next page.*

**WP277**

- Play each example three times:
  1. Have the student listen and determine which chords you played.
  2. Have the student listen again and circle the appropriate face (happy for Major and sad for minor).
  3. Have the student check his or her answer after the third hearing.
- Have the student play the chords in the correct place on the keyboard.

## UNIT 3   (pages 14-17)

### 16 RECOGNIZING INTERVALS

- Have the student identify the given notes.
- Tell the student you are going to play seconds or thirds up or down from the given notes.
- Play each example three times:
  1. Have the student listen and determine the second note you played.
  2. Have the student listen again and write the second note on the staff.
  3. Have the student check his or her answer after the third hearing.

*Note:* You may play the examples below or improvise your own depending on the needs and abilities of the student.

### 17 RHYTHM AND CHORDS

- Have the student write the names of the keys in the triangles and write the counts in all examples.
- Play each example three times:
  1. Have the student listen and determine which chords you played.
  2. Have the student listen again and circle the appropriate chords.
  3. Have the student check his or her answer after the third hearing.
- Have the student play the chords in the correct place on the keyboard.

## UNIT 4   (pages 18-21)

### 20 RECOGNIZING INTERVALS

- Have the student identify the given notes.
- Tell the student you are going to play seconds or thirds up or down from the given notes.
- Play each example three times:
  1. Have the student listen and determine the second note you played.
  2. Have the student listen again and write the second note on the staff.
  3. Have the student check his or her answer after the third hearing.

*Note:* You may play the examples below or improvise your own depending on the needs and abilities of the student.

### 21 RHYTHM AND CHORDS

- Have the student write the names of the keys in the triangles and write the counts in all examples.
- Play each example three times:
  1. Have the student listen and determine which chords you played.
  2. Have the student listen again and circle the appropriate chords.
  3. Have the student check his or her answer after the third hearing.
- Have the student play the chords in the correct place on the keyboard.

## UNIT 5 (pages 22-27)

### 26 RHYTHM AND CHORDS

- Have the student write the names of the keys in the triangles and write the counts in all examples.
- Play each example three times:
   1. Have the student listen and determine which chords you played.
   2. Have the student listen again and circle the appropriate chords.
   3. Have the student check his or her answer after the third hearing.
- Have the student play the chords in the correct place on the keyboard.

### 27 HAPPY OR SAD?

- Have the student write the counts in all examples.
- As a warm-up exercise, play several Major and minor chords and have the student identify the qualities.
- Relate the happy face to the sound of Major chords and the sad face to the sound of minor chords.
- Play each example three times:
   1. Have the student listen and determine which chords you played.
   2. Have the student listen again and circle the appropriate face (happy for Major and sad for minor).
   3. Have the student check his or her answer after the third hearing.
- Have the student play the chords in the correct place on the keyboard.

## UNIT 6 (pages 28-32)

### 30 BIRTHDAYS, SAINTS, BRIDES, OR STARS?

- Have the student write the names of the intervals in the triangles in all examples.
- To teach the sound of a specific interval, play and sing a familiar song that has that specific interval between the first two different pitches. Some suggestions:
   2nd: *Happy Birthday*
   3rd: *When the Saints Come Marching In*
   4th: *Here Comes the Bride*
   5th: *Twinkle, Twinkle, Little Star*
- Play each example three times:
   1. Have the student listen and determine what interval you played.
   2. Have the student listen again and circle the appropriate interval.
   3. Have the student check his or her answer after the third hearing.

### 31 RHYTHM AND CHORDS

- Have the student write the names of the keys in the triangles and write the counts in all examples.
- Play each example three times:
   1. Have the student listen and determine which chords you played.
   2. Have the student listen again and circle the appropriate chords.
   3. Have the student check his or her answer after the third hearing.
- Have the student play the chords in the correct place on the keyboard.

## 32 HEARING MELODIES

- Have the student identify the given notes.
- Explain that the rhythm above each example will match what you play and the student should listen and concentrate specifically on the tones in the melody.
- Play each example four times:
  1. Have the student listen and determine the direction (up or down).
  2. Have the student listen again and determine whether you played seconds, thirds, or repeated notes.
  3. Have the student listen again and write the notes you played on the staff in the correct rhythm.
  4. Have the student check his or her answer after the fourth hearing.

*Note:* You may play the examples below or improvise your own depending on the needs and abilities of the student.

## UNIT 7 (pages 33-38)

## 36 HEARING MELODIES

- Have the student identify the given notes.
- Explain that the rhythm above each example will match what you play and the student should listen and concentrate specifically on the tones in the melody.
- Play each example four times:
  1. Have the student listen and determine the direction (up or down).
  2. Have the student listen again and determine whether you played seconds, thirds, or repeated notes.
  3. Have the student listen again and write the notes you played on the staff in the correct rhythm.
  4. Have the student check his or her answer after the fourth hearing.

*Note:* You may play the examples below or improvise your own depending on the needs and abilities of the student.

## 37 RHYTHM AND CHORDS

- Have the student write the names of the keys in the triangles and write the counts in all examples.
- Play each example three times:
  1. Have the student listen and determine chords you played.
  2. Have the student listen again and circle the appropriate chords.
  3. Have the student check his or her answer after the third hearing.
- Have the student play the chords in the correct place on the keyboard.

## 38 HAPPY OR SAD?

- Have the student write the counts in all examples.
- As a warm-up exercise, play several Major and minor chords and have the student identify the qualities.
- Relate the happy face to the sound of Major chords and the sad face to the sound of the minor chords.
- Play each example three times:
  1. Have the student listen and determine which chords you played.
  2. Have the student listen again and circle the appropriate face (happy for Major and sad for minor).
  3. Have the student check his or her answer after the third hearing.
- Have the student play the chords in the correct place on the keyboard.